Pirate Paul & Ana Mae Mouse Show Me

# The Twelve Months Of™

# Michigan

Words and Illustrations by
AnnieMarie E. Chiaverilla

*Enjoy The Journey to* — *Chiaverilla*

The
Peartree Press™

*The Twelve Months of* ᴛᴍ *Michigan* is a trademark of AnnMarie E. Chiaverilla

A family of mice travel across Michigan in twelve months and are shown
the sights, learning about the great state of Michigan as they travel.

The Pear Tree Press, Inc.
2894 Lauryl Drive, Commerce Township, MI 48382
www.thepeartreepress.com | Ph: 810 844 6550

Editors: Katie McGrail and Angela Matthews

Words and illustrations © 2013 AnnMarie E. Chiaverilla.
Published by The Pear Tree Press, Inc.

Original black ink and water color: AnnMarie E. Chiaverilla
font: anniegirl

Mellito Bee appears courtesy of Paige and Company ᴛᴍ

ISBN 978-0-578-12988-4
Library of Congress Control Number: 2013915917
Printed in the United States of America.
Paper #2 domestic coated sheet.

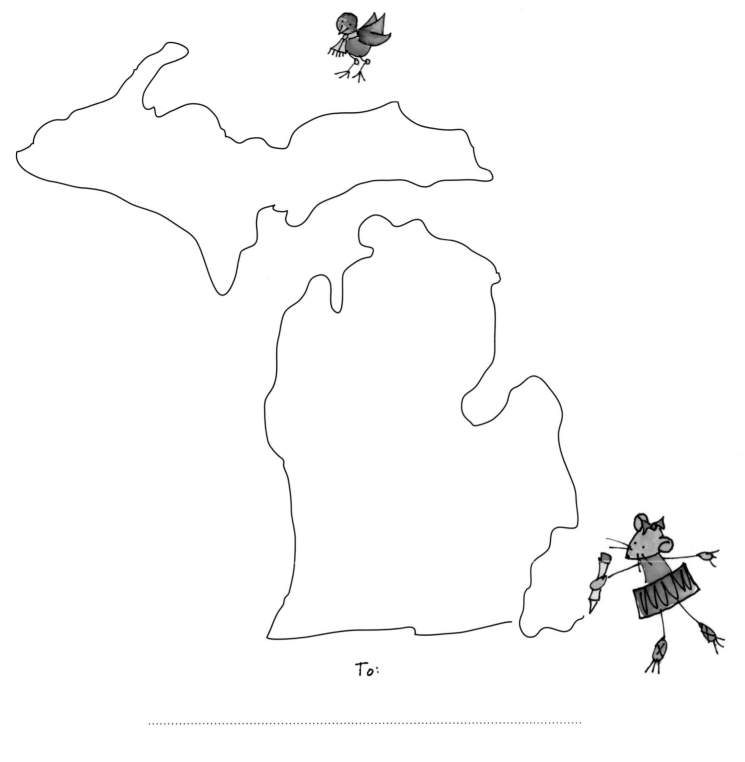

To:

.......................................................................................................

.......................................................................................................

From:

.......................................................................................................

♥

For my mom, Ana Mae and my dad Paul.
Thank you for showing me so many beautiful places
in the great state of Michigan,
and everything else.


and


A special thanks to you the reader, the explorer, whoever you are.
Have fun checking out our journey.


♥

Dear Reader,

This book is purely for giggles. It's not a complete collection of Michigan facts and figures. That would take way too long to draw and color and ... I'd rather giggle.

My parents, Pirate Paul and Ana Mae Mouse, showed my brothers, my sister and me some of the unique and beautiful places in the State of Michigan. I was lucky to have parents who enjoyed the outdoors and going for rides in the car. Our vacations were spent up north, most memorable to Mackinac Island and Drummond Island. The car rides with my siblings were terrifyingly fun.

I am very grateful for the adventures I shared with my family, and I thought you might like to hear our story. I hope this book inspires you and your family on your own special adventures.

With hugs and kisses,
AnnieMarie Mouse

# STATE SYMBOLS

State Flower - 1897, the APPLE BLOSSOM
(Pyrus coronaria)

State Bird - 1931, the AMERICAN ROBIN
(Turdus migratorius)

State Tree - 1955, the WHITE PINE
(Pinus strobus)

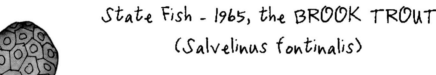

State Fish - 1965, the BROOK TROUT
(Salvelinus fontinalis)

State Stone - 1965, the PETOSKEY STONE
(Hexagonaria pericarnata)

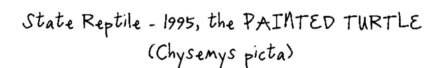

State Reptile - 1995, the PAINTED TURTLE
(Chysemys picta)

State Game Mammal - 1997, WHITE-TAILED DEER
(Odocoileus virginianus)

State Wildflower - 1998, DWARF LAKE IRIS
(Iris lacustris)

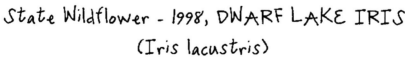

State Fossil - 2002, the MASTODON - (Mammut americanum)
found in more than 250 locations in the state

State Insect (unofficial) - Green Darner Dragonfly
(Anax junius)

Now you know, let's go!

Pirate Paul    Ana Mae

Michigan's State Motto:
"Si Quaeris Peninsulam Amoenam Circumspice"
"If you seek a pleasant peninsula, look about you."

In the first month
of Michigan,
my parents showed to me

a Robin in a White Pine Tree.

In the second month
of Michigan,
my parents showed to me

two Painted Turtles
and
a Robin in a White Pine Tree.

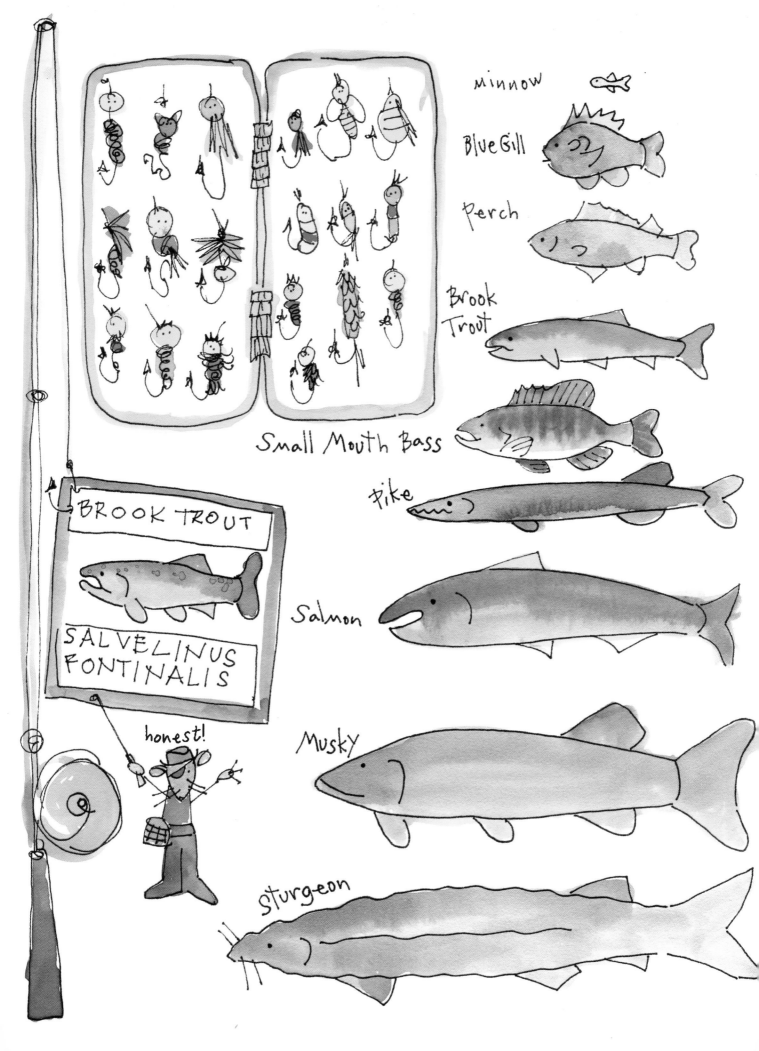

minnow

BlueGill

Perch

Brook Trout

Small Mouth Bass

Pike

BROOK TROUT

SALVELINUS FONTINALIS

honest!

Salmon

Musky

Sturgeon

In the third month
of Michigan,
my parents showed to me

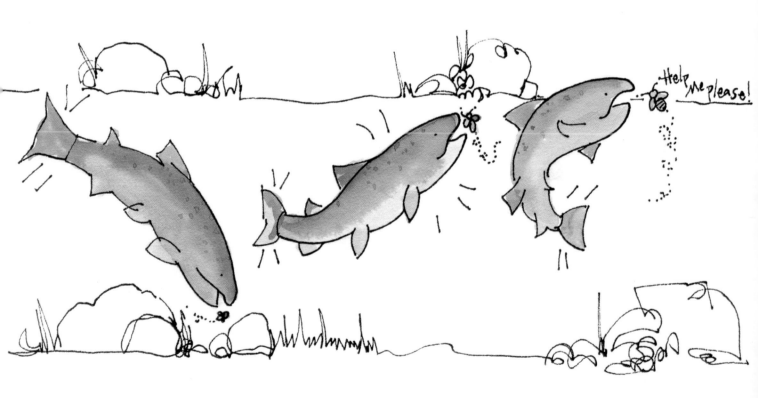

three Brook Trout, two Painted Turtles
and
a Robin in a White Pine Tree.

In the fourth month
of Michigan,
my parents showed to me

four Dragonflies,
three Brook Trout, two Painted Turtles
and
a Robin in a White Pine Tree.

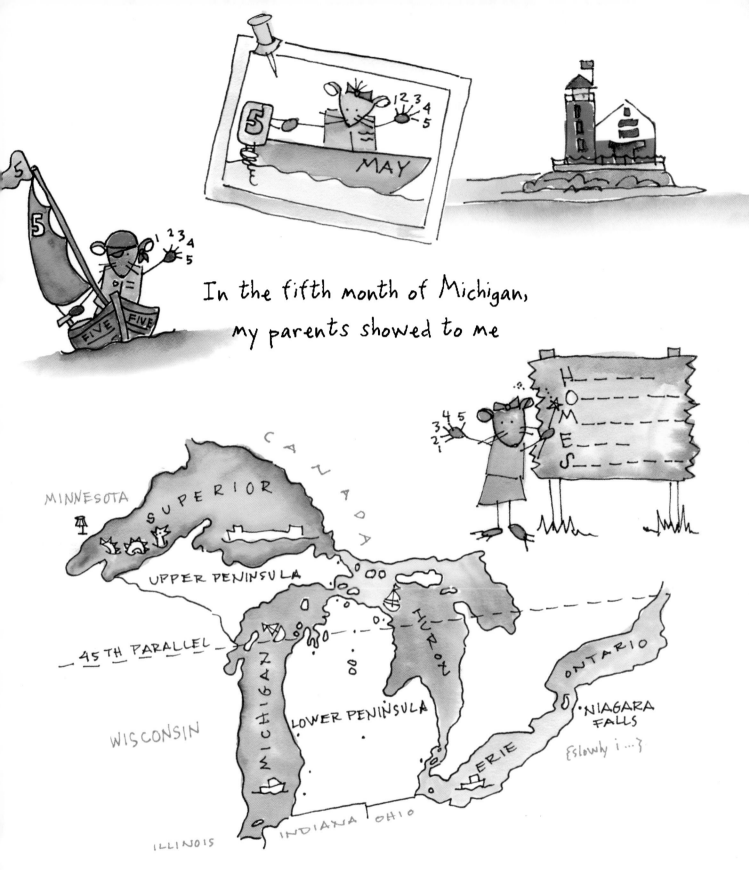

In the fifth month of Michigan,
my parents showed to me

**FIVE GREAT LAKES!**
four Dragonflies, three Brook Trout, two Painted Turtles
and
a Robin in a White Pine Tree.

PETOSKY STONE

HEXAGONARIA

ISLE ROYALE GREENSTONE

CHLORASTROLITE

STATE SAND

Kalkaska Sand

to dream!

STATE FOSSIL

American Mastadon-Probosideans

In the sixth month of Michigan,
my parents showed to me

six stones a-skipping,
**FIVE GREAT LAKES!**
four Dragonflies, three Brook Trout, two Painted Turtles
and
a Robin in a White Pine Tree.

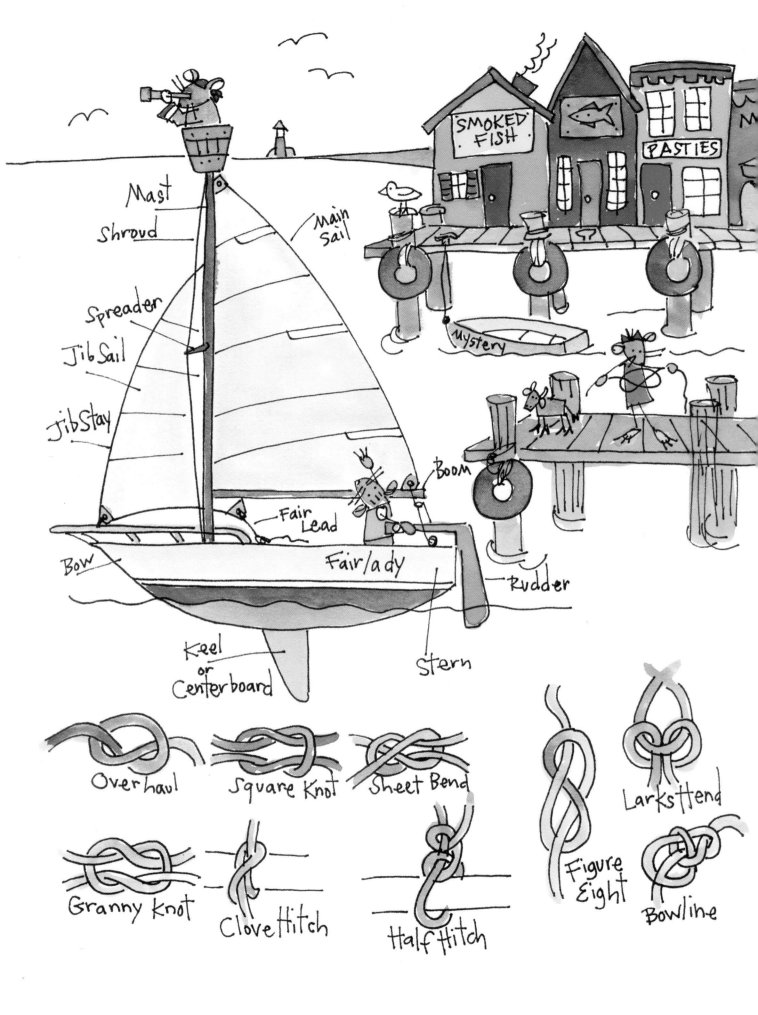

Mast
Shroud
Main Sail
Spreader
Jib Sail
Jib Stay
Boom
Fair Lead
Bow
Fair lady
Rudder
Keel or Centerboard
Stern
Mystery
SMOKED FISH
PASTIES

Overhaul
Square Knot
Sheet Bend
Larks Head
Granny Knot
Clove Hitch
Half Hitch
Figure Eight
Bowline

In the seventh month of Michigan,
my parents showed to me

seven boats a-sailing, six stones a-skipping,
**FIVE GREAT LAKES!**
four Dragonflies, three Brook Trout, two Painted Turtles
and
a Robin in a White Pine Tree.

# THE GARAGE

In the eighth month of Michigan,
my parents showed to me

eight cars a-cruising,
seven boats a-sailing, six stones a-skipping
**FIVE GREAT LAKES!**
four Dragonflies, three Brook Trout, two Painted Turtles
and
a Robin in a White Pine Tree.

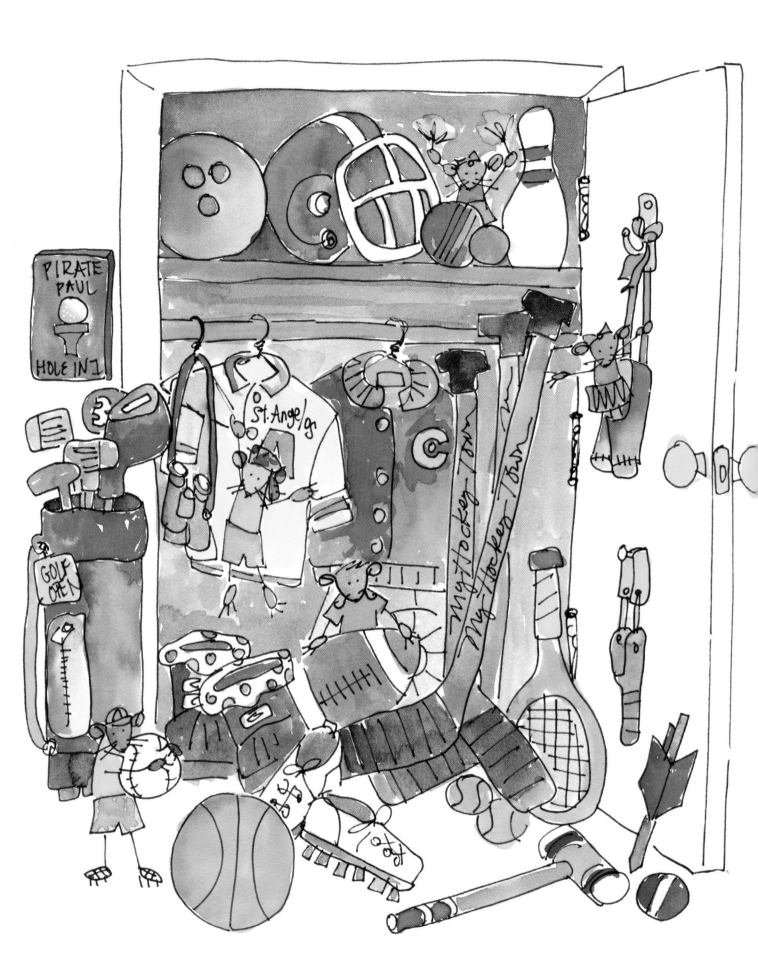

SEPTEMBER

In the ninth month of Michigan,
my parents showed to me

nine fans a-cheering,
eight cars a-cruising, seven boats a-sailing, six stones a-skipping,
**FIVE GREAT LAKES!**
four Dragonflies, three Brook Trout, two Painted Turtles
and
a Robin in a White Pine Tree.

**Ana Mae's Apple Pie Recipe**

Preheat oven 450 degrees

- 1 Box pre-made crust
  (prepare as directed)
- 3/4 cup sugar
- 2 teaspoon cinnamon
- 1 tablespoon flour
- 1/2 teaspoon salt
- 6 Granny Smith apples
- 1 pat of butter

Combine cinnamon, sugar, salt, and flour, mix together. Peel and slice apples and toss them in the dry ingredients till apples are coated.

Place mixture in pie shell add the pat of butter to the top of mixture. Add top crust and pinch around sides to seal crust together. Poke a few holes in the top of crust.

Bake 15 minutes on 450, reduce heat down to 350 and cover the edge of the crust with foil. Continue baking for another 45 minutes.

In the tenth month of Michigan,
my parents showed to me

ten pies a-baking,
nine fans a-cheering, eight cars a-cruising,
seven boats-a-sailing, six stones a-skipping,
**FIVE GREAT LAKES!**
four Dragonflies, three Brook Trout, two Painted Turtles
and
a Robin in a White Pine Tree.

In the eleventh month of Michigan,
my parents showed to me

eleven deer a-dancing,
ten pies a-baking, nine fans a-cheering,
eight cars a-cruising, seven boats a-sailing, six stones a-skipping,
**FIVE GREAT LAKES!**
four Dragonflies, three Brook Trout, two Painted Turtles
and
a Robin in a White Pine Tree.

In the twelfth month of Michigan,
my parents showed to me

twelve singers singing,
eleven deer a-dancing, ten pies a-baking, nine fans a-cheering,
eight cars a-cruising, seven boats a-sailing, six stones a-skipping,
**FIVE GREAT LAKES!**
four Dragonflies, three Brook Trout, two Painted Turtles
and
a Robin in a White Pine Tree.

The journey doesn't have to end here.
Continue exploring the great state of Michigan
with Pirate Paul and Ana Mae mouse at
thepeartreepress.com

Let me know why you
think your state is great